There are 2 groups of 3 (2x3=6).

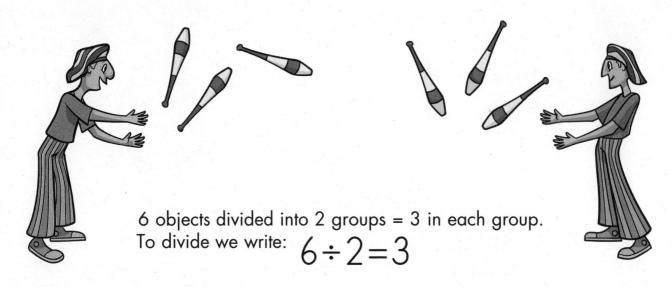

6 objects divided into 2 groups = 3 in each group.
To divide we write: $6 \div 2 = 3$

The answer to each division problem is called the **quotient.**
Write the quotient for each problem.

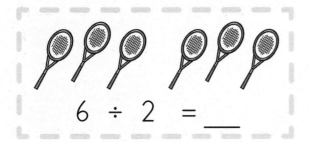

$6 \div 2 = \underline{}$

$8 \div 4 = \underline{}$

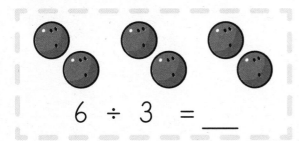

$6 \div 3 = \underline{}$

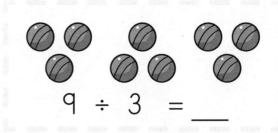

$9 \div 3 = \underline{}$

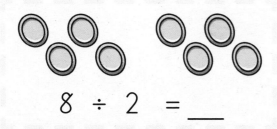

$8 \div 2 = \underline{}$

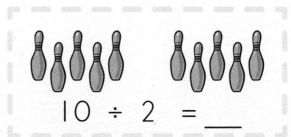

$10 \div 2 = \underline{}$

$$12 \div 4 = \underline{\hphantom{00}}$$

$$12 \div 2 = \underline{\hphantom{00}}$$

$$12 \div 6 = \underline{\hphantom{00}}$$

$$15 \div 3 = \underline{\hphantom{00}}$$

$$15 \div 5 = \underline{\hphantom{00}}$$

$$10 \div 5 = \underline{\hphantom{00}}$$

Fact Families

Once you know your multiplication facts, it is easy to divide.
Use fact families to help you find the quotient.

2×2 = ___

$4 \div 2$ = ___

3×3 = ___

$9 \div 3$ = ___

4×4 = ___

$16 \div 4$ = ___

2×5 = ___

$10 \div 2$ = ___

$10 \div 5$ = ___

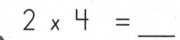

2×4 = ___

$8 \div 2$ = ___

$8 \div 4$ = ___

3×2 = ___

$6 \div 3$ = ___

$6 \div 2$ = ___

6×2 = ___

$12 \div 2$ = ___

$12 \div 6$ = ___

3 x 4 = __

12 ÷ 3 = __

12 ÷ 4 = __

7 x 2 = __

14 ÷ 2 = __

14 ÷ 7 = __

5 x 3 = __

15 ÷ 3 = __

15 ÷ 5 = __

8 x 2 = __

16 ÷ 2 = __

16 ÷ 8 = __

4 x 5 = __

20 ÷ 4 = __

20 ÷ 5 = __

9 x 2 = __

18 ÷ 2 = __

18 ÷ 9 = __

10 x 2 = __

20 ÷ 2 = __

20 ÷ 10 = __

Check
your
answers.

Divide any number by 1 and the quotient is always the other number.

$1 \div 1 =$ $6 \div 1 =$

$2 \div 1 =$ $7 \div 1 =$

$3 \div 1 =$ $8 \div 1 =$

$4 \div 1 =$ $9 \div 1 =$

$5 \div 1 =$ $10 \div 1 =$

Find your answers in the picture.

Divide any number by 2 and the quotient
is always one half the other number.

$2 \div 2 =$

$4 \div 2 =$

$6 \div 2 =$

$8 \div 2 =$

$10 \div 2 =$

$12 \div 2 =$

$14 \div 2 =$

$16 \div 2 =$

$18 \div 2 =$

$20 \div 2 =$

The human cannonball has been
divided in half! Draw to complete
the other half of the picture.

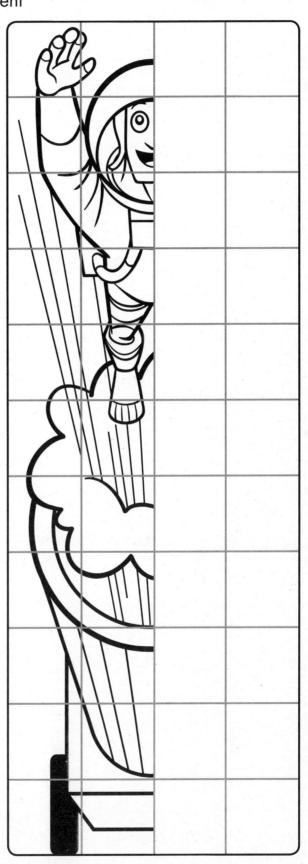

Start

$3 \div 3 =$

$9 \div 3 =$

$6 \div 3 =$

$15 \div 3 =$

$12 \div 3 =$

$18 \div 3 =$

$27 \div 3 =$

$24 \div 3 =$

$21 \div 3 =$

$30 \div 3 =$

Finish

Follow the numbers in the order of the quotients to help the clown find his shoes.

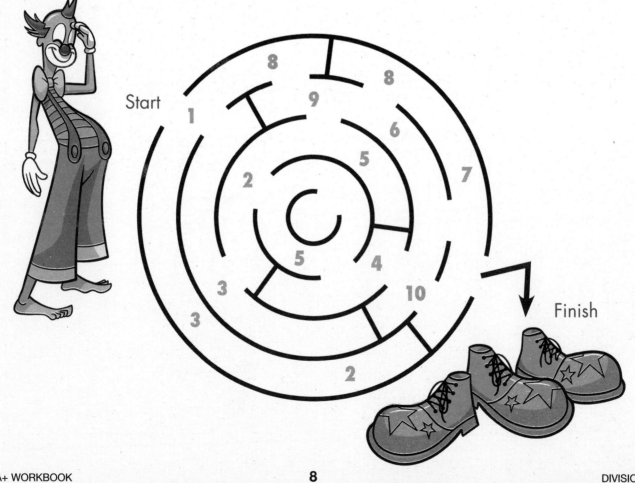

Start

Finish

quotient

$$6 \div 3 = 2$$ is the same as $3 \overline{)6}$
dividend divisor quotient   2

dividend divisor quotient   divisor dividend

$1\overline{)4}$ $2\overline{)6}$ 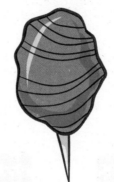 $2\overline{)16}$

$2\overline{)4}$ $3\overline{)6}$ $3\overline{)12}$ $1\overline{)1}$ $1\overline{)6}$

$1\overline{)3}$  $2\overline{)12}$ $3\overline{)24}$ $3\overline{)21}$

$3\overline{)18}$ $1\overline{)2}$ $2\overline{)14}$ $2\overline{)18}$

$1\overline{)8}$ $2\overline{)8}$ $3\overline{)9}$  $1\overline{)7}$

$3\overline{)3}$ $1\overline{)9}$ $2\overline{)10}$ $2\overline{)20}$

4 ÷ 4 =
red=

36 ÷ 4 =
purple=

8 ÷ 4 =
yellow=

28 ÷ 4 =
brown=

24 ÷ 4 =
pink=

40 ÷ 4 =
black=

32 ÷ 4 =
blue=

16 ÷ 4 =
green=

12 ÷ 4 =
orange=

20 ÷ 4 =
gray=

Use the code to color the picture.

$5 \div 5 =$
A=

$40 \div 5 =$
S=

$15 \div 5 =$
B=

$20 \div 5 =$
I=

$35 \div 5 =$
T=

$30 \div 5 =$
N=

$25 \div 5 =$
U=

$10 \div 5 =$
C=

$45 \div 5 =$
R=

$50 \div 5 =$
E=

Which planet is like a circus?

Use the code to find out.

$$\overline{8} \ \overline{1} \ \overline{7} \ \overline{5} \ \overline{9} \ \overline{6} \ ,$$

$$\overline{3} \ \overline{10} \ \overline{2} \ \overline{1} \ \overline{5} \ \overline{8} \ \overline{10}$$

$$\overline{4} \ \overline{7} \ \overset{H}{\overline{}} \ \overline{1} \ \overline{8} \ \overline{9} \ \overline{4} \ \overline{6} \ \overset{G}{\overline{8}} \ \overset{!}{\overline{}}$$

$18 \div 6 =$ ☐ $24 \div 6 =$ ☐

$6 \div 6 =$ ☐ $42 \div 6 =$ ☐

$54 \div 6 =$ ☐ $60 \div 6 =$ ☐

$12 \div 6 =$ ☐ $30 \div 6 =$ ☐

$36 \div 6 =$ ☐ $48 \div 6 =$ ☐

Follow the problems with quotients less than 6 to get the clown to his costume.

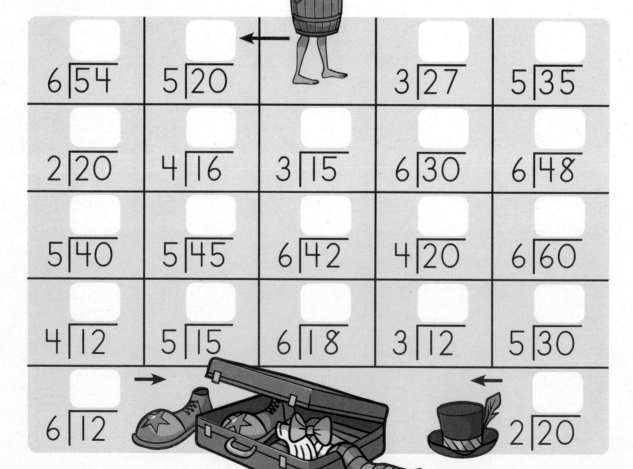

$6\overline{)54}$	$5\overline{)20}$		$3\overline{)27}$	$5\overline{)35}$
$2\overline{)20}$	$4\overline{)16}$	$3\overline{)15}$	$6\overline{)30}$	$6\overline{)48}$
$5\overline{)40}$	$5\overline{)45}$	$6\overline{)42}$	$4\overline{)20}$	$6\overline{)60}$
$4\overline{)12}$	$5\overline{)15}$	$6\overline{)18}$	$3\overline{)12}$	$5\overline{)30}$
$6\overline{)12}$				$2\overline{)20}$

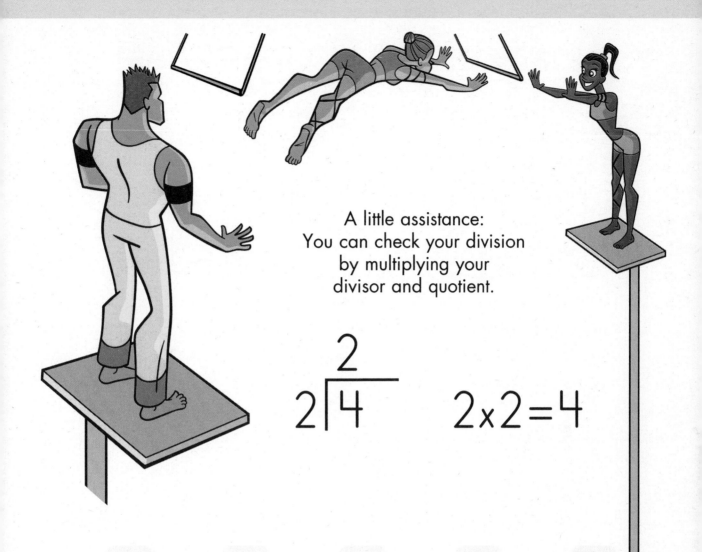

A little assistance:
You can check your division
by multiplying your
divisor and quotient.

$$2\overline{)4}^{\,2} \qquad 2 \times 2 = 4$$

$5\overline{)10}$ $\quad$ $4\overline{)28}$ $\quad$ $4\overline{)36}$ $\quad$ $5\overline{)50}$ $\quad$ $4\overline{)8}$

$4\overline{)40}$ $\quad$ $6\overline{)6}$ $\quad$ $5\overline{)25}$ $\quad$ $6\overline{)24}$ $\quad$ $6\overline{)36}$

$6\overline{)48}$ $\quad$ $4\overline{)20}$ $\quad$ $5\overline{)30}$ $\quad$ $5\overline{)15}$ $\quad$ $4\overline{)32}$

$21 \div 7 =$

$14 \div 7 =$

$35 \div 7 =$

$42 \div 7 =$

$49 \div 7 =$

$7 \div 7 =$

$28 \div 7 =$

$56 \div 7 =$

$70 \div 7 =$

$63 \div 7 =$

The Flying Wallendas have performed high-wire acts for generations. Look up, down, across, backward, and diagonally for these Wallenda family names:

Karl	Alida	Tino
Carla	Sandra	Nikolas
Herman	Rick	Delilah
Helen	Edith	Mario

```
M  N  A  M  R  E  H  Z
A  L  I  D  A  A  T  I
R  I  C  K  L  M  I  N
I  A  A  I  O  A  D  G
O  R  L  N  E  L  E  H
L  E  I  A  L  R  A  C
D  T  A  R  D  N  A  S
```

Complete this sentence by counting up the number of letters NOT used in the word find.

The Wallendas are famous for performing a 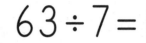 - person pyramid atop the wire.

$80 \div 8 =$ 　　　　$16 \div 8 =$

$32 \div 8 =$ 　　　　$40 \div 8 =$

$56 \div 8 =$ 　　　　$64 \div 8 =$

$8 \div 8 =$ 　　　　$48 \div 8 =$

$24 \div 8 =$ 　　　　$72 \div 8 =$

Divide. Then follow the arrows
to help the clown find his tricycle.
Add up the numbers you land on.

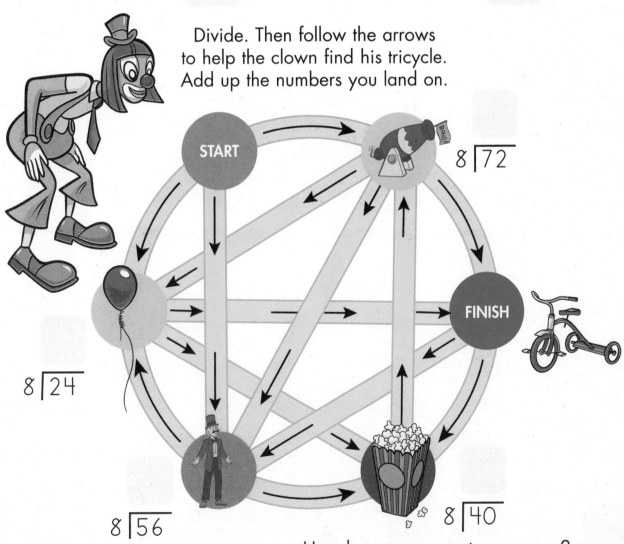

START

$8\overline{)72}$

FINISH

$8\overline{)24}$

$8\overline{)56}$

$8\overline{)40}$

How low can you get your score?

$27 \div 9 =$
T=

$18 \div 9 =$
I=

$45 \div 9 =$
A=

$63 \div 9 =$
M=

$81 \div 9 =$
C=

$9 \div 9 =$
B=

$36 \div 9 =$
O=

$72 \div 9 =$
E=

$54 \div 9 =$
H=

$90 \div 9 =$
G=

What happened to the boy who ran
away with the circus?

Use the code to find out.

$$\overline{3}\ \overline{6}\ \overline{8}\ \overset{P}{\overline{4}}\ \overset{L}{\overline{2}}\ \overline{9}\ \overline{8}$$

$$\overline{7}\ \overline{5}\ \overset{D}{\overline{8}}\ \overline{6}\ \overline{2}\ \overline{7}$$

$$\overline{1}\ \overset{R}{\overline{2}}\ \overset{N}{\overline{10}}\ \overline{2}\ \overline{3}\ \overline{1}\ \overline{5}\ \overset{K.}{\overline{9}}$$

Start

$30 \div 10 =$ $20 \div 10 =$

$10 \div 10 =$ $40 \div 10 =$

$50 \div 10 =$ $70 \div 10 =$

$80 \div 10 =$ $100 \div 10 =$

$60 \div 10 =$ $90 \div 10 =$

Finish

Follow the numbers in the order of the quotients.

Circus Fun Facts!

The oldest record of a clown dates to ☐ 500 BC in Egypt.

8⟌16

In 2005, Anthony Gatto juggled ☐ clubs for ☐ minutes, 38 seconds.

4⟌24   9⟌63

Karl Wallenda started performing acrobatic stunts at age ☐.

6⟌36

Joseph Grimaldi, the Father of Modern Clowning, first performed on stage at age ☐.

7⟌21

There are ☐ types of clowns in major clown competitions.

8⟌32

The admission price for the first Ringling Bros. Circus in 1870 was ☐ ¢.

3⟌3

Their circus was started by ☐ of the seven Ringling brothers.

5⟌25

The first trapeze act was performed by Jules Léotard in France in 1 ☐ 5 ☐.

2⟌16   9⟌81

In French Trapeze, ☐ performers work together on a single trapeze.

3⟌6

Ready for a challenge? Write the missing divisors, dividends, and quotients.

$3\overline{)24}$ □

$5\overline{)\,}$ 3

□ $4\overline{)16}$

$6\overline{)42}$ □

$2\overline{)20}$ □

$4\overline{)\,}$ 5

□ $6\overline{)12}$

$10\overline{)90}$ □

$5\overline{)15}$ □

$8\overline{)\,}$ 2

□ $2\overline{)10}$

$6\overline{)54}$ □

A In circus-talk, what is a funambulist?

B What color facepaint do clowns consider unlucky?

A. a high-wire performer

B. blue

$18 \div 6 =$

$42 \div 7 =$

$12 \div 3 =$

$5 \div 5 =$

$15 \div 5 =$

$72 \div 9 =$

$42 \div 6 =$

$40 \div 4 =$

$9 \div 3 =$

$18 \div 9 =$

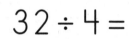

$12 \div 2 =$

$32 \div 4 =$

$24 \div 4 =$

$36 \div 9 =$

$8 \div 2 =$

$36 \div 6 =$

$48 \div 8 =$

$2 \div 2 =$

$70 \div 7 =$

$72 \div 8 =$

$12 \div 4 =$

$35 \div 7 =$

$20 \div 2 =$

$21 \div 3 =$

 $8 \div 8 =$

$24 \div 6 =$

$30 \div 5 =$

 $45 \div 9 =$

$81 \div 9 =$

$8 \div 1 =$

$2 \div 1 =$

 $14 \div 7 =$

$80 \div 10 =$

$24 \div 8 =$

$6 \div 3 =$

$18 \div 2 =$

$60 \div 10 =$

$25 \div 5 =$

$28 \div 4 =$

$63 \div 9 =$

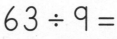

$2\overline{)12}$ $8\overline{)24}$ $9\overline{)27}$ $2\overline{)16}$

$6\overline{)42}$ $5\overline{)25}$ $3\overline{)24}$ $8\overline{)8}$

$10\overline{)50}$ $3\overline{)6}$ $7\overline{)21}$ $5\overline{)20}$

$9\overline{)63}$ $6\overline{)48}$ $2\overline{)20}$ $8\overline{)72}$

$7\overline{)14}$ $3\overline{)18}$ $10\overline{)80}$ $4\overline{)12}$

$2\overline{)6}$ $4\overline{)32}$ $4\overline{)24}$ $5\overline{)40}$

$6\overline{)24}$ $7\overline{)56}$ $9\overline{)36}$ $9\overline{)81}$

$3\overline{)12}$ $7\overline{)49}$ $3\overline{)15}$ $8\overline{)56}$

$10\overline{)20}$ $8\overline{)48}$ $2\overline{)18}$ $4\overline{)28}$

$6\overline{)54}$ $5\overline{)35}$ $2\overline{)8}$ $9\overline{)18}$

Divide. Follow the path with quotients of 4 to get the family of 4 to the stands. Then follow the path with quotients of 5 to get the family of 5 to the stands.

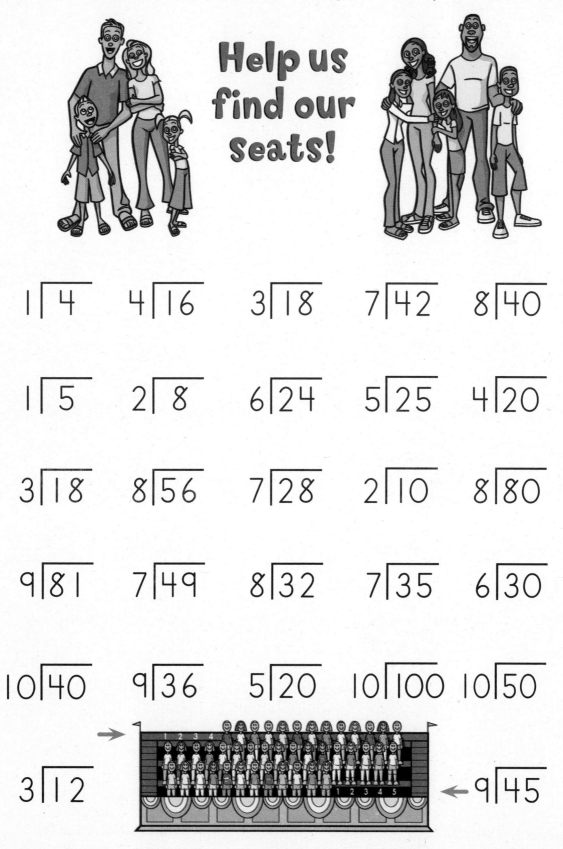

Help us find our seats!

$1\overline{)4}$ $4\overline{)16}$ $3\overline{)18}$ $7\overline{)42}$ $8\overline{)40}$

$1\overline{)5}$ $2\overline{)8}$ $6\overline{)24}$ $5\overline{)25}$ $4\overline{)20}$

$3\overline{)18}$ $8\overline{)56}$ $7\overline{)28}$ $2\overline{)10}$ $8\overline{)80}$

$9\overline{)81}$ $7\overline{)49}$ $8\overline{)32}$ $7\overline{)35}$ $6\overline{)30}$

$10\overline{)40}$ $9\overline{)36}$ $5\overline{)20}$ $10\overline{)100}$ $10\overline{)50}$

$3\overline{)12}$ $9\overline{)45}$

$9\overline{)}$ quotient 9

$8\overline{)56}$

$\overline{)14}$ quotient 7

$1\overline{)}$ quotient 9

$8\overline{)32}$

$\overline{)35}$ quotient 7

$6\overline{)}$ quotient 10

$8\overline{)64}$

$\overline{)48}$ quotient 8

$9\overline{)}$ quotient 4

$8\overline{)8}$

$\overline{)27}$ quotient 3

$7\overline{)}$ quotient 6

$10\overline{)100}$

$\overline{)42}$ quotient 7

$3\overline{)}$ quotient 9

$6\overline{)24}$

$\overline{)56}$ quotient 8

$5\overline{)}$ quotient 9

$4\overline{)12}$

$\overline{)80}$ quotient 8

$6\overline{)}$ quotient 9

$7\overline{)49}$

$\overline{)40}$ quotient 5

$10\overline{)}$ quotient 9

$7\overline{)28}$

$\overline{)16}$ quotient 8

$3\overline{)}$ quotient 5

$7\overline{)63}$

$\overline{)72}$ quotient 8

$10\overline{)}$ quotient 3

$8\overline{)72}$

$\overline{)63}$ quotient 9

$4\overline{)}$ quotient 6

$3\overline{)18}$

Use these steps to divide larger numbers.

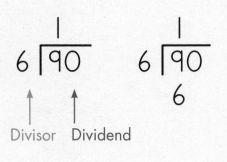

$$
\begin{array}{r}
1 \\
6\overline{)90}
\end{array}
\qquad
\begin{array}{r}
1 \\
6\overline{)90} \\
6
\end{array}
\qquad
\begin{array}{r}
1 \\
6\overline{)90} \\
-6\downarrow \\
\hline
30
\end{array}
\qquad
\begin{array}{r}
15 \\
6\overline{)90} \\
-6 \\
\hline
30 \\
30
\end{array}
\qquad
\begin{array}{r}
15 \\
6\overline{)90} \\
-6 \\
\hline
30 \\
-30 \\
\hline
0
\end{array}
$$

Divisor Dividend

1. Divide the tens.

2. Multiply and write the answer.

3. Subtract and bring down the ones column number.

4. Is the divisor smaller than the dividend? If so, divide again.

5. Subtract. If you end up with zero, you've found the quotient.

$5\overline{)85}$ $9\overline{)99}$ $8\overline{)96}$ $2\overline{)34}$

$3\overline{)87}$ $7\overline{)91}$ $4\overline{)56}$ $6\overline{)78}$

Sometimes you don't end up with zero after dividing. Write R for **remainder** and write the leftover amount at the end of the quotient.

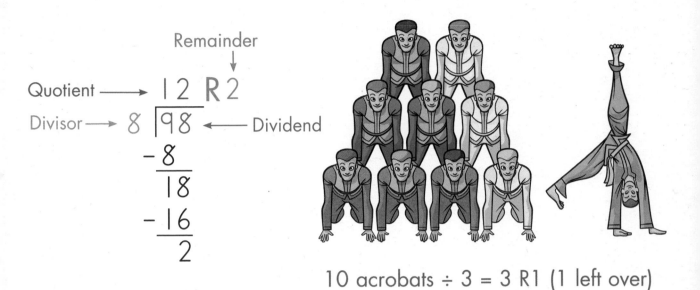

Quotient ⟶ 12 R 2 ← Remainder
Divisor ⟶ 8 |98 ← Dividend
$$\begin{array}{r} 12\ R2 \\ 8\overline{)98} \\ -8 \\ \hline 18 \\ -16 \\ \hline 2 \end{array}$$

10 acrobats ÷ 3 = 3 R1 (1 left over)

$7\overline{)92}$ R

$2\overline{)31}$ R

$3\overline{)41}$ R

$5\overline{)72}$ R

$6\overline{)83}$ R

$9\overline{)86}$ R

Word Problems

Read each story. Decide whether to **multiply** or **divide**. Write the problem and the answer.

Mike brought 10 children to the circus. He bought 30 snacks. How many snacks did each child get?

Problem

$$30 \div 10 = ?$$

Answer

3

Snacks

The acrobat can do 6 flips in one minute. How many flips can she do in 9 minutes?

Problem

Answer

Flips

Each juggler has 7 clubs. There are 49 clubs in all. How many jugglers are there?

Problem

Answer

Jugglers

Tony went to the circus 4 days in a row. Each day he bought 5 balloons. How many balloons did he buy all together?

Problem

Answer

Balloons

A clown performed for 6 days. He performed 7 stunts each day. How many stunts did he perform all together?

Problem

Answer

Stunts

Rachel can't wait for the circus—it is coming in 28 days! How many weeks is that?

Problem

Answer

_____ Weeks

Rachel's mom told her that for every 10 chores Rachel finished, she could invite 1 friend to the circus. Rachel finished 60 chores before circus day. How many friends could she invite?

Problem

Answer

_____ Friends

Rachel's mom bought 8 circus tickets. The tickets cost $4.00 each. How much did her mother spend in all?

Problem

Answer

_____ Dollars

Rachel brought 6 friends with her to the circus. She bought 34 pieces of candy. She split them up evenly between her friends. How many pieces of candy did her friends get? How many pieces were left over for Rachel?

Problem

Answers

_____ Pieces of candy for each friend

_____ Left over

Answers page 2

Introduction to Division

There are 2 groups of 3 (2x3=6).

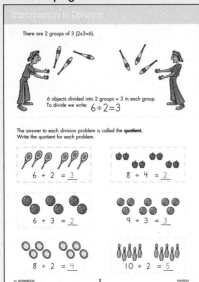

6 objects divided into 2 groups = 3 in each group.
To divide we write: 6÷2=3

The answer to each division problem is called the **quotient**.
Write the quotient for each problem.

6 ÷ 2 = 3   8 ÷ 4 = 2

6 ÷ 3 = 2   9 ÷ 3 = 3

8 ÷ 2 = 4   10 ÷ 2 = 5

A+ WORKBOOK   2   DIVISION

Answers page 3

12 ÷ 4 = 3

12 ÷ 2 = 6

12 ÷ 6 = 2

15 ÷ 3 = 5

15 ÷ 5 = 3

10 ÷ 5 = 2

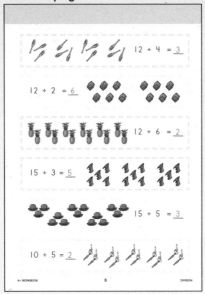

A+ WORKBOOK   3   DIVISION

Answers page 4

Fact Families

Once you know your multiplication facts, it is easy to divide.
Use fact families to help you find the quotient.

3 x 2 = 6   2 x 3 = 6   6 ÷ 2 = 3   6 ÷ 3 = 2

2 x 2 = 4   3 x 3 = 9   4 x 4 = 16
4 ÷ 2 = 2   9 ÷ 3 = 3   16 ÷ 4 = 4

2 x 5 = 10   Welcome, families!   2 x 4 = 8
10 ÷ 2 = 5   8 ÷ 2 = 4
10 ÷ 5 = 2   8 ÷ 4 = 2

3 x 2 = 6   6 x 2 = 12
6 ÷ 3 = 2   12 ÷ 2 = 6
6 ÷ 2 = 3   12 ÷ 6 = 2

A+ WORKBOOK   4   DIVISION

Answers page 5

3 x 4 = 12   7 x 2 = 14
12 ÷ 3 = 4   14 ÷ 2 = 7
12 ÷ 4 = 3   14 ÷ 7 = 2

5 x 3 = 15   8 x 2 = 16
15 ÷ 3 = 5   16 ÷ 2 = 8
15 ÷ 5 = 3   16 ÷ 8 = 2

4 x 5 = 20   9 x 2 = 18
20 ÷ 4 = 5   18 ÷ 2 = 9
20 ÷ 5 = 4   18 ÷ 9 = 2

10 x 2 = 20
20 ÷ 2 = 10
20 ÷ 10 = 2

Check your answers.

A+ WORKBOOK   5   DIVISION

Answers page 6

Divide by 1

Divide any number by 1 and the quotient is always the other number.

1 ÷ 1 = 1   6 ÷ 1 = 6
2 ÷ 1 = 2   7 ÷ 1 = 7
3 ÷ 1 = 3   8 ÷ 1 = 8
4 ÷ 1 = 4   9 ÷ 1 = 9
5 ÷ 1 = 5   10 ÷ 1 = 10

Find your answers in the picture.

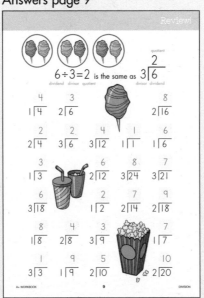

A+ WORKBOOK   6   DIVISION

Answers page 7

Divide by 2

Divide any number by 2 and the quotient
is always one half the other number.

2 ÷ 2 = 1
4 ÷ 2 = 2
6 ÷ 2 = 3
8 ÷ 2 = 4
10 ÷ 2 = 5
12 ÷ 2 = 6
14 ÷ 2 = 7
16 ÷ 2 = 8
18 ÷ 2 = 9
20 ÷ 2 = 10

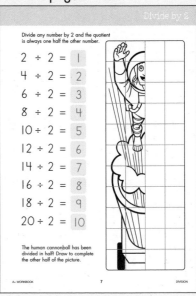

The human cannonball has been
divided in half! Draw to complete
the other half of the picture.

A+ WORKBOOK   7   DIVISION

Answers page 8

Divide by 3

3 ÷ 3 = 1   18 ÷ 3 = 6
9 ÷ 3 = 3   27 ÷ 3 = 9
6 ÷ 3 = 2   24 ÷ 3 = 8
15 ÷ 3 = 5   21 ÷ 3 = 7
12 ÷ 3 = 4   30 ÷ 3 = 10

Follow the numbers in the order of the quotients to help the clown find his shoes.

A+ WORKBOOK   8   DIVISION

Answers page 9

Review!

6÷3=2 is the same as 3)6
dividend divisor quotient   divisor dividend

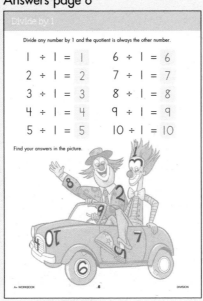

$$\begin{array}{cc} 4 & 3 \\ 1\overline{)4} & 2\overline{)6} \end{array}$$

8
2)16

2   2   4   1   6
2)4   3)6   3)12   1)1   1)6

3   6   8   7
1)3   2)12   3)24   3)21

6   7   9
3)18   1)12   2)14   2)18

8   4   3   7
1)8   2)8   3)9   1)7

1   9   5   10
3)3   1)9   2)10   2)20

A+ WORKBOOK   9   DIVISION

Answers page 10

Divide by 4

4 ÷ 4 = 1 red=   36 ÷ 4 = 9 purple=
8 ÷ 4 = 2 yellow=   28 ÷ 4 = 7 brown=
24 ÷ 4 = 6 pink=   40 ÷ 4 = 10 black=
32 ÷ 4 = 8 blue=   16 ÷ 4 = 4 green=
12 ÷ 4 = 3 orange=   20 ÷ 4 = 5 gray=

Use the code to color the picture.

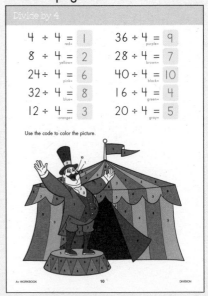

A+ WORKBOOK   10   DIVISION

Answers page 11

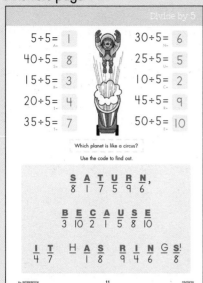

Divide by 5

5÷5 = 1	30÷5 = 6
40÷5 = 8	25÷5 = 5
15÷5 = 3	10÷5 = 2
20÷5 = 4	45÷5 = 9
35÷5 = 7	50÷5 = 10

Which planet is like a circus?

Use the code to find out.

$\underset{8}{S}\underset{1}{A}\underset{7}{T}\underset{5}{U}\underset{9}{R}\underset{6}{N},$

$\underset{3}{B}\underset{10}{E}\underset{2}{C}\underset{1}{A}\underset{5}{U}\underset{8}{S}\underset{10}{E}$

$\underset{4}{I}\underset{7}{T} \quad \underset{1}{H}\underset{8}{A}\underset{}{S} \quad \underset{9}{R}\underset{4}{I}\underset{6}{N}\underset{8}{G}S!$

A+ WORKBOOK   11   DIVISION

Answers page 12

Divide by 6

18 ÷ 6 = 3	24 ÷ 6 = 4
6 ÷ 6 = 1	42 ÷ 6 = 7
54 ÷ 6 = 9	60 ÷ 6 = 10
12 ÷ 6 = 2	30 ÷ 6 = 5
36 ÷ 6 = 6	48 ÷ 6 = 8

Follow the problems with quotients less than 6 to get the clown to his costume.

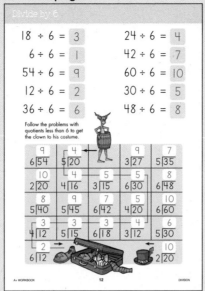

A+ WORKBOOK   12   DIVISION

Answers page 13

Review!

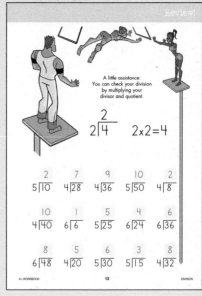

A little assistance:
You can check your division
by multiplying your
divisor and quotient.

$2\overline{)4}^{2} \quad 2 \times 2 = 4$

$5\overline{)10}^{2}$	$4\overline{)28}^{7}$	$4\overline{)36}^{9}$	$5\overline{)50}^{10}$	$4\overline{)8}^{2}$
$4\overline{)40}^{10}$	$6\overline{)6}^{1}$	$5\overline{)25}^{5}$	$6\overline{)24}^{4}$	$6\overline{)36}^{6}$
$6\overline{)48}^{8}$	$4\overline{)20}^{5}$	$5\overline{)30}^{6}$	$5\overline{)15}^{3}$	$4\overline{)32}^{8}$

A+ WORKBOOK   13   DIVISION

Answers page 14

Divide by 7

21÷7 = 3	7÷7 = 1
14÷7 = 2	28÷7 = 4
35÷7 = 5	56÷7 = 8
42÷7 = 6	70÷7 = 10
49÷7 = 7	63÷7 = 9

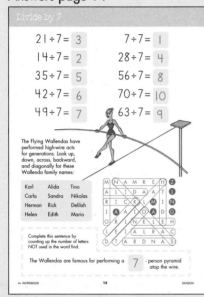

The Flying Wallendas have performed high-wire acts for generations. Look up, down, across, backward, and diagonally for these Wallenda family names:

Karl   Alida   Tino
Carla   Sandra   Nikolas
Herman Rick   Delilah
Helen   Edith   Mario

Complete this sentence by counting up the number of letters NOT used in the word find.

The Wallendas are famous for performing a 7 - person pyramid atop the wire.

A+ WORKBOOK   14   DIVISION

Answers page 15

Divide by 8

80÷8 = 10	16÷8 = 2
32÷8 = 4	40÷8 = 5
56÷8 = 7	64÷8 = 8
8÷8 = 1	48÷8 = 6
24÷8 = 3	72÷8 = 9

Divide. Then follow the arrows to help the clown find his tricycle. Add up the numbers you land on.

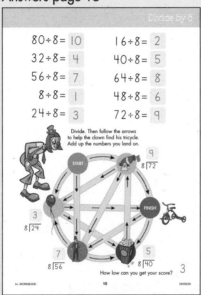

$8\overline{)72}^{9}$

$8\overline{)24}^{3}$

$8\overline{)56}^{7}$

$8\overline{)40}^{5}$

How low can you get your score? 3

A+ WORKBOOK   15   DIVISION

Answers page 16

Divide by 9

27÷9 = 3	9÷9 = 1
18÷9 = 2	36÷9 = 4
45÷9 = 5	72÷9 = 8
63÷9 = 7	54÷9 = 6
81÷9 = 9	90÷9 = 10

What happened to the boy who ran away with the circus?

Use the code to find out.

$\underset{3}{T}\underset{6}{H}\underset{8}{E} \quad \underset{4}{P}\underset{2}{O}\underset{9}{L}\underset{8}{I}\underset{}{C}\underset{}{E}$

$\underset{7}{M}\underset{5}{A}\underset{8}{D}\underset{6}{E} \quad \underset{2}{H}\underset{7}{I}\underset{}{M}$

$\underset{1}{B}\underset{2}{R}\underset{10}{I}\underset{2}{N}\underset{3}{G} \quad \underset{1}{I}\underset{5}{T} \quad \underset{9}{B}\underset{}{A}\underset{}{C}\underset{}{K}.$

A+ WORKBOOK   16   DIVISION

Answers page 17

Divide by 10

Start

30 ÷ 10 = 3	20 ÷ 10 = 2
10 ÷ 10 = 1	40 ÷ 10 = 4
50 ÷ 10 = 5	70 ÷ 10 = 7
80 ÷ 10 = 8	100 ÷ 10 = 10
60 ÷ 10 = 6	90 ÷ 10 = 9

Finish

Follow the numbers in the order of the quotients.

A+ WORKBOOK   17   DIVISION

Answers page 18

Circus Fun Facts!

The oldest record of a clown dates to 2 500 BC in Egypt.
$8\overline{)16}$

In 2005, Anthony Gatto juggled 6 clubs for 7 minutes, 38 seconds.
$4\overline{)24}$ $9\overline{)63}$

Karl Wallenda started performing acrobatic stunts at age 6
$6\overline{)36}$

Joseph Grimaldi, the Father of Modern Clowning, first performed on stage at age 3
$7\overline{)21}$

There are 4 types of clowns in major clown competitions.
$8\overline{)32}$

The admission price for the first Ringling Bros. Circus in 1870 was 1 ¢.
$3\overline{)3}$

Their circus was started by 5 of the seven Ringling brothers.
$5\overline{)25}$

The first trapeze act was performed by Jules Léotard in France in 1 8 5 9.
$2\overline{)16}$ $9\overline{)81}$

In French Trapeze, 2 performers work together on a single trapeze.
$3\overline{)6}$

A+ WORKBOOK   18   DIVISION

Answers page 19

Challenge

Ready for a challenge? Write the missing divisors, dividends, and quotients.

$3\overline{)24}^{8}$ $5\overline{)15}^{3}$ A

In circus talk, what is a funambulist?

$4\overline{)16}^{4}$ $6\overline{)42}^{7}$

$2\overline{)20}^{10}$ $4\overline{)20}^{5}$

$2\overline{)12}^{6}$ $10\overline{)90}^{9}$ B

What color pompoms do clowns consider unlucky?

$5\overline{)15}^{3}$ $8\overline{)16}^{2}$

$5\overline{)10}^{2}$ $6\overline{)54}^{9}$

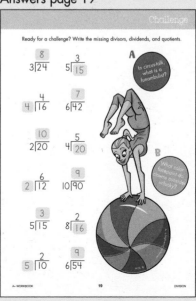

A+ WORKBOOK   19   DIVISION

Skill Builder

18 ÷ 6 = 3   42 ÷ 7 = 6
12 ÷ 3 = 4   5 ÷ 5 = 1
15 ÷ 5 = 3   72 ÷ 9 = 8
42 ÷ 6 = 7   40 ÷ 4 = 10
9 ÷ 3 = 3   18 ÷ 9 = 2
12 ÷ 2 = 6   32 ÷ 4 = 8
24 ÷ 4 = 6   36 ÷ 9 = 4
8 ÷ 2 = 4   36 ÷ 6 = 6
48 ÷ 8 = 6   2 ÷ 2 = 1
70 ÷ 7 = 10   72 ÷ 8 = 9

A+ WORKBOOK   20   DIVISION

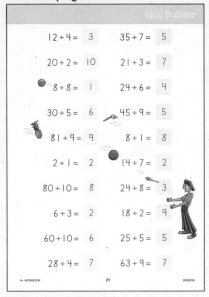

Skill Builder

12 ÷ 4 = 3   35 ÷ 7 = 5
20 ÷ 2 = 10   21 ÷ 3 = 7
8 ÷ 8 = 1   24 ÷ 6 = 4
30 ÷ 5 = 6   45 ÷ 9 = 5
81 ÷ 9 = 9   8 ÷ 1 = 8
2 ÷ 1 = 2   14 ÷ 7 = 2
80 ÷ 10 = 8   24 ÷ 8 = 3
6 ÷ 3 = 2   18 ÷ 2 = 9
60 ÷ 10 = 6   25 ÷ 5 = 5
28 ÷ 4 = 7   63 ÷ 9 = 7

A+ WORKBOOK   21   DIVISION

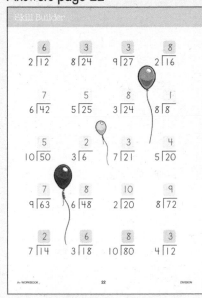

Skill Builder

Problem	Quotient
2)12	6
8)24	3
9)27	3
2)16	8
6)42	7
5)25	5
3)24	8
8)8	1
10)50	5
3)6	2
7)21	3
5)20	4
9)63	7
6)48	8
2)20	10
8)72	9
7)14	2
3)18	6
10)80	8
4)12	3

A+ WORKBOOK   22   DIVISION

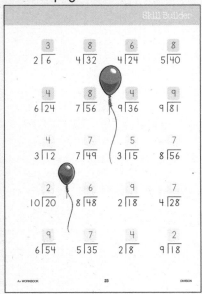

Skill Builder

Problem	Quotient
2)6	3
4)32	8
4)24	6
5)40	8
6)24	4
7)56	8
9)36	4
9)81	9
3)12	4
7)49	7
3)15	5
8)56	7
10)20	2
8)48	6
2)18	9
4)28	7
6)54	9
5)35	7
2)8	4
9)18	2

A+ WORKBOOK   23   DIVISION

Review

Divide. Follow the path with quotients of 4 to get the family of 4 to the stands. Then follow the path with quotients of 5 to get the family of 5 to the stands.

Help us find our seats!

1)4 = 4 ; 4)16 = 4 ; 3)18 = 6 ; 7)42 = 6 ; 8)40 = 5
1)5 = 5 ; 2)8 = 4 ; 6)24 = 4 ; 5)25 = 5 ; 4)20 = 5
3)18 = 6 ; 8)56 = 7 ; 7)28 = 4 ; 2)10 = 5 ; 8)80 = 10
9)81 = 9 ; 7)49 = 7 ; 8)32 = 4 ; 7)35 = 5 ; 6)30 = 5
10)40 = 4 ; 9)36 = 4 ; 5)20 = 4 ; 10)100 = 10 ; 10)50 = 5
3)12 = 4 ; 9)45 = 5

A+ WORKBOOK   24   DIVISION

Challenge

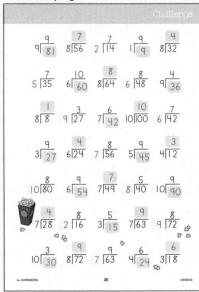

9)81 = 9 ; 8)56 = 7 ; 2)14 = 7 ; 1)9 = 9 ; 8)32 = 4
5)35 = 7 ; 6)60 = 10 ; 8)64 = 8 ; 6)48 = 8 ; 9)36 = 4
8)8 = 1 ; 9)27 = 3 ; 7)42 = 6 ; 10)100 = 10 ; 6)42 = 7
3)27 = 9 ; 6)24 = 4 ; 7)56 = 8 ; 5)45 = 9 ; 4)12 = 3
10)80 = 8 ; 6)54 = 9 ; 7)49 = 7 ; 8)40 = 5 ; 10)90 = 9
7)28 = 4 ; 2)16 = 8 ; 3)15 = 5 ; 7)63 = 9 ; 9)72 = 8
10)30 = 3 ; 8)72 = 9 ; 7)63 = 9 ; 4)24 = 6 ; 3)18 = 6

A+ WORKBOOK   25   DIVISION

Challenge! Long Division

Use these steps to divide larger numbers.

$$\begin{array}{r}1\\6)\overline{90}\end{array} \quad \begin{array}{r}1\\6)\overline{90}\\6\end{array} \quad \begin{array}{r}1\\6)\overline{90}\\-6\downarrow\\\overline{30}\end{array} \quad \begin{array}{r}15\\6)\overline{90}\\-6\\\overline{30}\\30\end{array} \quad \begin{array}{r}15\\6)\overline{90}\\-6\\\overline{30}\\-30\\\overline{0}\end{array}$$

Divisor   Dividend

1. Divide the tens.
2. Multiply and write the answer.
3. Subtract and bring down the ones column number.
4. Is the divisor smaller than the dividend? If so, divide again.
5. Subtract. If you end up with zero, you've found the quotient.

$$\begin{array}{r}17\\5)\overline{85}\\-5\\\overline{35}\\-35\\\overline{0}\end{array} \quad \begin{array}{r}11\\9)\overline{99}\\-9\\\overline{9}\\-9\\\overline{0}\end{array} \quad \begin{array}{r}12\\8)\overline{96}\\-8\\\overline{16}\\-16\\\overline{0}\end{array} \quad \begin{array}{r}17\\2)\overline{34}\\-2\\\overline{14}\\-14\\\overline{0}\end{array}$$

$$\begin{array}{r}29\\3)\overline{87}\\-6\\\overline{27}\\-27\\\overline{0}\end{array} \quad \begin{array}{r}13\\7)\overline{91}\\-7\\\overline{21}\\-21\\\overline{0}\end{array} \quad \begin{array}{r}14\\4)\overline{56}\\-4\\\overline{16}\\-16\\\overline{0}\end{array} \quad \begin{array}{r}13\\6)\overline{78}\\-6\\\overline{18}\\-18\\\overline{0}\end{array}$$

A+ WORKBOOK   26   DIVISION

Challenge! Division with Remainders

Sometimes you don't end up with zero after dividing. Write R for **remainder** and write the leftover amount at the end of the quotient.

Remainder

$$\begin{array}{r}12\ \text{R}2\\8)\overline{98}\\-8\\\overline{18}\\-16\\\overline{2}\end{array}$$

Quotient →   Divisor →   ← Dividend

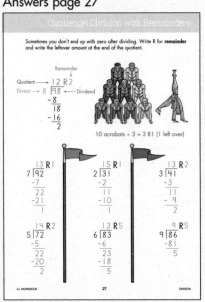

10 acrobats ÷ 3 = 3 R1 (1 left over)

$$\begin{array}{r}13\ \text{R}1\\7)\overline{92}\\-7\\\overline{22}\\-21\\\overline{1}\end{array} \quad \begin{array}{r}15\ \text{R}1\\2)\overline{31}\\-2\\\overline{11}\\-10\\\overline{1}\end{array} \quad \begin{array}{r}13\ \text{R}2\\3)\overline{41}\\-3\\\overline{11}\\-9\\\overline{2}\end{array}$$

$$\begin{array}{r}14\ \text{R}2\\5)\overline{72}\\-5\\\overline{22}\\-20\\\overline{2}\end{array} \quad \begin{array}{r}13\ \text{R}5\\6)\overline{83}\\-6\\\overline{23}\\-18\\\overline{5}\end{array} \quad \begin{array}{r}9\ \text{R}5\\9)\overline{86}\\-81\\\overline{5}\end{array}$$

A+ WORKBOOK   27   DIVISION

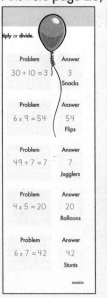

Multiply or divide.

Problem	Answer
30 ÷ 10 = 3	3 Snacks
6 × 9 = 54	54 Flips
49 ÷ 7 = 7	7 Jugglers
4 × 5 = 20	20 Balloons
6 × 7 = 42	42 Stunts

Problem	Answer
28 ÷ 7 = 4	4 Weeks
60 ÷ 10 = 6	6 Friends
8 × 4 = 32	32 Dollars
6)34 = 5 R4, -30, 4	5 Pieces of candy for each friend; 4 Left over

DIVISION

Illustrated by: Greg Hardin